The Gardener's Yearbook

PUBLISHED BY THE READER'S DIGEST ASSOCIATION LIMITED

LONDON • NEW YORK • SYDNEY • CAPE TOWN • MONTREAL

A READER'S DIGEST BOOK
Published by the Reader's Digest Association Limited
Berkeley Square House
Berkeley Square
London W1X 6AB

ISBN 0 276 42322 4

This book is based on an American concept, *Successful Gardening Journal*,
produced by the Reader's Digest Association, Inc.
US Editor: Carolyn T. Chubet
US Designer: Elizabeth L. Tunnicliffe
US Writer-Consultant: Thomas Christopher
Adapted for the UK by Tucker Slingsby Ltd, London

Cover and interior photographs:
Winter: D. Phillips/TCL/Masterfile, USA
Spring: Mike Coltman/TCL/Masterfile, USA
Autumn: Geoff Dufeu/TCL/Masterfile, USA
Summer: Ron Rovtar/Photonica, USA

Printed and bound in Great Britain by Butler & Tanner Ltd
Frome and London

TABLE OF CONTENTS

We must cultivate our garden.
— Voltaire, *Candide*

HOW TO USE YOUR GARDENING YEARBOOK

Experienced gardeners know that some of their most important work is done not with a spade but with a pencil and a yearbook like this one. For good record keeping is at the heart of successful gardening – your notes enable you to build on past triumphs and to avoid repeating mistakes. This attractive yearbook is the perfect place to record what is happening in your garden each week and to keep a note of purchases and plantings. This information will be invaluable when you come to plan changes and improvements.

THE GARDENER'S YEARBOOK is divided into four seasonal sections: winter, spring, summer and autumn – each one introduced by inspirational poetry and quotations specially chosen to appeal to gardeners. Each section is then subdivided into months and has weekly fill-in pages that prompt you to record essential information such as the weather, soil conditions, plants in flower, the state of the lawn, what needs doing in the greenhouse and other important tasks. If you spend a little time each week writing in these sections, you will have a personal record of events and gardening activities to guide you

 the following year and for years after that. Additional space for your own notes is provided on each page and on the seasonal notes' pages included at the end of each season. These pages are the ideal place to jot down notes and ideas – perhaps the name of a new plant you would like to buy or a planting scheme you have seen in another garden and which you would like to try in your own.

And since successful gardening is in large part a matter of timing, the seasonal pages also provide a checklist of tasks which need to be undertaken each month to keep your garden looking its best. Full details of how to complete all these jobs, with explanatory step-by-step illustrations where necessary, are given in the Reader's Digest book NEW GARDENING YEAR.

Following the seasonal pages is a special section of plant and vegetable profiles, offering a place to keep more detailed notes on individual plants or crops. These records will be invaluable when it comes to assessing which plants you should grow again and which have done less well in the soil and weather conditions in your garden.

Take a moment to browse through the yearbook and you will see how easy it is to fill in each week and how very useful it will be. Happy gardening!

WINTER

Sometimes hath the brightest day a cloud;

And after summer evermore succeeds

Barren winter, with his wrathful nipping cold:

So cares and joys abound, as seasons fleet.

—William Shakespeare, *Henry VI*

*I have often wondered that those who...
love to live in gardens, have never
thought of contriving a Winter Garden,
which should consist of such trees only as
never cast their leaves....I have so far
indulged myself in this thought, that I
have set apart a whole acre of ground for
the executing of it. The walls are covered
with ivy....The laurel, the hornbeam,
and the holly, with many other trees and
plants...grow so thick in it, that you
cannot imagine a more lively scene.*

—Joseph Addison, *The Spectator*

FOR YOU THERE'S
ROSEMARY AND RUE;
THESE KEEP
SEEMING AND SAVOUR ALL
THE WINTER LONG.

—William Shakespeare,
The Winter's Tale

Weather _____

Soil Conditions _____

In Flower _____

_____

Beds & Borders _____

Greenhouse _____

Fruit & Vegetables _____

Lawn _____

Trees & Shrubs _____

Notes _____

_____

C H E C K L I S T

- ❏ Check stakes and ties on newly planted trees to make sure they are secure and not rubbing.
- ❏ Keep an area of the pond ice free if you keep fish.
- ❏ Lag or drain outdoor pipes.
- ❏ Protect newly planted shrubs and shrubs of borderline hardiness by covering them with an insulating material such as horticultural fleece, plastic bubblewrap or straw.
- ❏ Clean and service the lawnmower and other garden tools.

Weather _____

Soil Conditions _____

In Flower _____

_____

Beds & Borders _____

Greenhouse _____

Fruit & Vegetables _____

Lawn _____

Trees & Shrubs _____

Notes _____

_____

❏ Check bulbs being forced for early flowering to make sure they don't dry out and that they are given light and warmth at the right time.

❏ Prune winter-flowering shrubs over three years old after flowering.

❏ Order or buy seeds of those plants that need to be sown in mid and late winter to ensure they get the long growing season they need.

❏ Check stored dahlia tubers for disease and dispose of any that are shrivelling or rotting.

DECEMBER

Weather _____

Soil Conditions _____

In Flower _____

_____

Beds & Borders _____

Greenhouse _____

Fruit & Vegetables _____

Lawn _____

Trees & Shrubs _____

Notes _____

_____

C H E C K L I S T

- ❏ Prune apple and pear trees and treat the cuts with a wound paint.
- ❏ Check that fuchsias packed in compost for the winter do not become completely dry and protect the crowns of hardy fuchsias outdoors with garden compost.

- ❏ Open the greenhouse ventilators on sunny days but close them early in the afternoon before the temperature drops.
- ❏ Check plants in the greenhouse, in cold frames and under cloches to see if they need watering.

Weather _____

Soil Conditions _____

In Flower _____

_____

Beds & Borders _____

Greenhouse _____

Fruit & Vegetables _____

Lawn _____

Trees & Shrubs _____

Notes _____

_____

❑ Lift rhubarb roots for forcing indoors and start forcing selected crowns outdoors.

❑ Clear and dig beds for use next spring provided the ground is not waterlogged or frozen.

❑ Keep the garden tidy and weed free to give overwintering pests fewer places to shelter.

❑ Use cold winter days when it is not possible to work outdoors to plan design improvements and new plantings for the spring.

Weather _____

Soil Conditions _____

In Flower _____

_____

Beds & Borders _____

Greenhouse _____

Fruit & Vegetables _____

Lawn _____

Trees & Shrubs _____

Notes _____

_____

C H E C K L I S T

- ❏ Protect vulnerable plants from frost and wind damage.
- ❏ Firm in any autumn-planted shrubs and border plants lifted by frost.
- ❏ Brush heavy snow from shrubs, conifers and hedges so that there is no danger of branches breaking.
- ❏ Order seeds, summer bulbs, plants and seedlings.
- ❏ Sow under glass half-hardy annuals that are slow to mature.
- ❏ Cut back clinging climbers from windows and doors.

Weather _____

Soil Conditions _____

In Flower _____

_____

Beds & Borders _____

Greenhouse _____

Fruit & Vegetables _____

Lawn _____

Trees & Shrubs _____

Notes _____

_____

- ❏ Deadhead and tidy plants in containers. Move pots containing vulnerable plants under cover if severe frosts are forecast.

- ❏ Germinate seeds such as begonias and pelargoniums on windowsills indoors or in the greenhouse.

- ❏ Cut down newly planted canes of raspberries, blackberries and hybrids to within 25–30 cm (10–12 in) of the ground.

- ❏ Ensure fuchsias overwintering in leaf in the greenhouse get as much light as possible and are not becoming pale and leggy.

Weather _____

Soil Conditions _____

In Flower _____

_____

Beds & Borders _____

Greenhouse _____

Fruit & Vegetables _____

Lawn _____

Trees & Shrubs _____

Notes _____

_____

C H E C K L I S T

- ❏ Complete the pruning of greenhouse vines while they are still dormant and remove loose bark which may harbour pests.
- ❏ Bring in pots of forced bulbs for indoor flowering when ready.

- ❏ Protect winter-flowering bulbous irises in the garden from severe cold or damp.
- ❏ Keep off the lawn when it is frozen or very wet.
- ❏ Start forcing pots of lily bulbs for Easter and early summer flowering.

Weather _____

Soil Conditions _____

In Flower _____

_____

Beds & Borders _____

Greenhouse _____

Fruit & Vegetables _____

Lawn _____

Trees & Shrubs _____

Notes _____

_____

❏ Pinch out rhododendron and azalea buds damaged by frost to prevent the spread of disease.

❏ Cut out broken, diseased, dead or rubbing branches on established trees and shrubs except *Prunus*.

❏ Wash and disinfect seed trays and pots, ready for early spring sowing and planting.

❏ Make any necessary repairs to structures supporting plants such as trellises, pergolas and arches while the plants are dormant.

Weather _____

Soil Conditions _____

In Flower _____

_____

Beds & Borders _____

Greenhouse _____

Fruit & Vegetables _____

Lawn _____

Trees & Shrubs _____

Notes _____

_____

C H E C K L I S T

- ❏ Use a soil thermometer to test the soil temperature. It is safest not to sow anything outdoors until the soil temperature has remained above 7°C (45°F) for a week.

- ❏ Test the soil in your garden to see if the pH needs adjusting or if it is deficient in any major nutrients.

- ❏ Put cloches in position to warm the soil for early sowings of vegetables next month.

- ❏ Sow under glass slow maturing bedding plants such as African marigolds, petunias, lobelia and antirrhinums.

Weather _____

Soil Conditions _____

In Flower _____

_____

Beds & Borders _____

Greenhouse _____

Fruit & Vegetables _____

Lawn _____

Trees & Shrubs _____

Notes _____

_____

❏ Keep the garden free from fallen leaves and other debris over the winter both to make it look more attractive and to deprive over–wintering pests of places to hide.

❏ Sow under glass quick-growing perennials to flower this year.

❏ Begin to feed plants in established borders using a controlled-release slow-acting fertiliser; try not to get fertiliser on the new foliage.

❏ Spray nectarine and peach trees to prevent or eradicate peach leaf curl disease.

Weather _____

Soil Conditions _____

In Flower _____

_____

Beds & Borders _____

Greenhouse _____

Fruit & Vegetables _____

Lawn _____

Trees & Shrubs _____

Notes _____

_____

C H E C K L I S T

- ❏ Bring strawberries in containers into the greenhouse for early fruit.
- ❏ Prune half-hardy fuchsias being kept under cover as soon as the pink 'eyes' (embryo shoots) appear.
- ❏ Sow seeds of tomatoes for growing in a cool greenhouse.

- ❏ Prick out or pot up pelargonium seedlings that have grown from seeds sown last month.
- ❏ Apply a top dressing of gravel or chippings around plants in the rock garden to suppress weeds and ensure free drainage.

Weather _____

Soil Conditions _____

In Flower _____

_____

Beds & Borders _____

Greenhouse _____

Fruit & Vegetables _____

Lawn _____

Trees & Shrubs _____

Notes _____

_____

- ❑ Sow sweet peas outdoors in their flowering position except in very cold areas.

- ❑ Clear weeds from around the base of established hedges and cut back overgrown deciduous hedges.

- ❑ Prune all shrubs, such as winter-flowering viburnums, which have just finished flowering if necessary.

- ❑ Clean and oil the blades of cutting tools. Check electrical equipment before the busy spring season.

WINTER
NOTES

SPRING

The thirsty earth soaks up the rain,

And drinks, and gapes for drink again.

The plants suck in the earth, and are

With constant drinking fresh and fair.

—Abraham Cowley, *Anacreon*

For winter's rains and ruins are over,

And all the season of snows and sins;

The days dividing lover and lover,

The light that loses, the night that wins;

And time remembered is grief forgotten,

And frosts are slain and flowers begotten,

And in green underwood and cover

Blossom by blossom the spring begins.

—Algernon Charles Swinburne
Atalanta in Calydon

BUT EACH SPRING...
A GARDENING INSTINCT,
SURE AS THE SAP RISING
IN THE TREES, STIRS
WITHIN US.

WE LOOK ABOUT AND
DECIDE TO TAME ANOTHER
LITTLE BIT OF GROUND.

—Lewis Gannett

Weather _____

Soil Conditions _____

In Flower _____

_____

Beds & Borders _____

Greenhouse _____

Fruit & Vegetables _____

Lawn _____

Trees & Shrubs _____

Notes _____

_____

C H E C K L I S T

- ❏ Sow hardy annuals in a cold frame or unheated greenhouse.
- ❏ Sow tender bedding plants in a heated propagator or in trays on a warm windowsill.
- ❏ Lift and divide congested clumps of perennials.

- ❏ Plant out bulbs grown for indoor use which have finished flowering.
- ❏ Mulch beds and borders while the soil is moist to reduce the need for watering and to keep down weeds.
- ❏ Prune roses removing decaying, old and thin, spindly wood.

Weather

Soil Conditions

In Flower

Beds & Borders

Greenhouse

Fruit & Vegetables

Lawn

Trees & Shrubs

Notes

- ❏ Take chrysanthemum cuttings.
- ❏ Remove shoots that have no live buds from summer-flowering clematis and cut back late-flowering clematis hard.
- ❏ Prune tender climbers and wall shrubs if they show strong growth.
- ❏ Remove winter protection from containers and top dress or replant overgrown or pot-bound plants, adding a slow-release fertiliser.
- ❏ Sow dahlia seeds to germinate in gentle heat and prick out seedlings when large enough to handle.

Weather	
Soil Conditions	
In Flower	
Beds & Borders	
Greenhouse	
Fruit & Vegetables	
Lawn	
Trees & Shrubs	
Notes	

C H E C K L I S T

- ❑ Prune plum trees once they have started growing.
- ❑ Make sure pots and seed trays in the greenhouse do not dry out.
- ❑ Cut off dead flower spikes from summer-flowering heathers and prune young tree heathers.

- ❑ Make the first outdoor sowings of culinary and salad herbs.
- ❑ Apply a spring fertiliser to established lawns once they are actively growing and cut grass when it is about 8 cm (3 in) high.
- ❑ Deadhead daffodils as they fade.

Weather _____

Soil Conditions _____

In Flower _____

_____

Beds & Borders _____

Greenhouse _____

Fruit & Vegetables _____

Lawn _____

Trees & Shrubs _____

Notes _____

_____

❏ Prune spring-flowering shrubs over three years old as they finish flowering.

❏ Sow sweet peas directly into their flowering position.

❏ Sprout maincrop potatoes and plant sprouted tubers of early varieties.

❏ Sow and plant out vegetables including beetroot, broad beans, carrots, celeriac, kohlrabi, onions, peas, spinach, swedes and turnips.

❏ Sow seeds of tomatoes in a heated propagator or on a warm windowsill to grow on outdoors when all danger of frost is over.

Weather _____

Soil Conditions _____

In Flower _____

_____

Beds & Borders _____

Greenhouse _____

Fruit & Vegetables _____

Lawn _____

Trees & Shrubs _____

Notes _____

_____

C H E C K   L I S T

- ❏ Begin to harden off young plants and overwintered cuttings.
- ❏ Remove the insulation from the greenhouse.
- ❏ Apply spring fertilisers, weedkillers and mosskillers to established lawns.

- ❏ Prune tender climbers and wall shrubs before leaves open fully.
- ❏ Plant summer hanging baskets and windowboxes but keep under cover till all danger of frost is past.
- ❏ Plant up herbs in containers.

Weather _____

Soil Conditions _____

In Flower _____

_____

Beds & Borders _____

Greenhouse _____

Fruit & Vegetables _____

Lawn _____

Trees & Shrubs _____

Notes _____

_____

❏ Apply slow-release fertiliser to containers and then mulch.

❏ Cut back hardy fuchsias to just above soil level as strong new basal growth appears.

❏ Start to sow hardy annuals directly into their flowering position.

❏ Plant tomatoes to grow in a cool greenhouse; train them up tall canes or strings.

❏ Sow melons and cucumbers under glass.

❏ Prune winter-flowering heathers as the flowers fade.

Weather _____

Soil Conditions _____

In Flower _____

_____

Beds & Borders _____

Greenhouse _____

Fruit & Vegetables _____

Lawn _____

Trees & Shrubs _____

Notes _____

_____

C H E C K L I S T

- ❏ Mow the lawn weekly or more often if necessary; frequent mowing encourages dense growth.
- ❏ Plant summer-flowering bulbs such as acidanthera and tigridia.
- ❏ Weed patios, paths and drives.
- ❏ Apply rose fertiliser, gently hoeing it in around the plants.
- ❏ Ventilate cold frames and the greenhouse whenever possible to encourage sturdy plant growth.
- ❏ Feed newly planted hedges.

Weather _____

Soil Conditions _____

In Flower _____

_____

Beds & Borders _____

Greenhouse _____

Fruit & Vegetables _____

Lawn _____

Trees & Shrubs _____

Notes _____

_____

❏ Continue to plant vegetables directly into the ground and under glass for a succession of crops.

❏ Fit collars around the stems of young cabbages, cauliflowers and Brussels sprouts to deter cabbage root fly.

❏ Earth up early potatoes.

❏ Prune spring-flowering shrubs over three years old as they finish flowering.

❏ Clean out the pond if necessary.

❏ Put new aquatic plants in the pond either in the soil at the bottom or using special aquatic baskets.

Weather _____

Soil Conditions _____

In Flower _____

_____

Beds & Borders _____

Greenhouse _____

Fruit & Vegetables _____

Lawn _____

Trees & Shrubs _____

Notes _____

_____

C H E C K L I S T

- ❏ Sow fast-maturing and late-flowering annuals directly into their flowering position.

- ❏ Move overwintered hardy annuals to their final flowering position.

- ❏ Water and feed plants in the greenhouse regularly.

- ❏ Feed seedlings and young plants which are growing poorly or have pale, yellowing foliage.

- ❏ Remove faded flowers from daffodils, hyacinths and tulips.

- ❏ Stake border plants to provide support as they grow.

Weather _____

Soil Conditions _____

In Flower _____

_____

Beds & Borders _____

Greenhouse _____

Fruit & Vegetables _____

Lawn _____

Trees & Shrubs _____

Notes _____

_____

❏ Take cuttings from summer-flowering clematis.

❏ Plant out annual climbers.

❏ Begin feeding plants in containers and continue through the summer.

❏ Harden off hanging baskets and windowboxes ready to put in position outdoors when all danger of frost is over.

❏ Plant both dormant dahlia tubers and young plants.

Weather _____

Soil Conditions _____

In Flower _____

_____

Beds & Borders _____

Greenhouse _____

Fruit & Vegetables _____

Lawn _____

Trees & Shrubs _____

Notes _____

_____

C H E C K L I S T

❏ Make sure fruit trees and bushes have sufficient water while the fruit is setting otherwise fruitlets are often shed.

❏ Cover the ground under strawberries with straw or matting to protect the ripening fruit from mud and from slugs and other pests.

❏ Feed newly shooting hardy fuchsias with a nitrogenous fertiliser and keep the base free from weeds.

❏ Organise shading for the greenhouse using blinds, shading nets or a shading wash.

Weather _____

Soil Conditions _____

In Flower _____

_____

Beds & Borders _____

Greenhouse _____

Fruit & Vegetables _____

Lawn _____

Trees & Shrubs _____

Notes _____

_____

- ❏ Plant out hardened off annuals when all danger of frost is over.
- ❏ Sow French and runner beans and erect supports for climbing beans.
- ❏ Start to cut lawns with naturalised bulbs; make the first cut high.
- ❏ Harden off aubergines, courgettes, marrows, peppers, pumpkins and tomatoes grown from seed before planting outside.
- ❏ Prune deciduous spring-flowering shrubs over three years old as they finish flowering.

NOTES

SPRING
NOTES

SUMMER

Now the summer came to pass

And flowers through the grass

Joyously sprang

While all the tribes of birds sang.

—Walther Von Der Vogelweide (c. 1160–1230), *Dream Song*

Soon will the high Midsummer
pomps come on,
Soon will the musk carnations
break and swell,

Soon shall we have gold-dusted
snapdragon,
Sweet-William with his
homely cottage-smell,
And stocks in fragrant blow;

Roses that down the alleys shine afar,
And open, jasmine-muffled lattices,
And groups under the dreaming
garden-trees,

And the full moon, and the white
evening-star.

—Matthew Arnold
Thyrsis

I SHOULD LIKE TO
ENJOY THIS SUMMER
FLOWER BY FLOWER,
AS IF IT WERE TO
BE THE LAST ONE
FOR ME.

—André Gide
Journals

Weather _____

Soil Conditions _____

In Flower _____

_____

Beds & Borders _____

Greenhouse _____

Fruit & Vegetables _____

Lawn _____

Trees & Shrubs _____

Notes _____

_____

C H E C K L I S T

- ❏ Sow seeds of fast-maturing annuals directly into the ground and thin any seedlings sown earlier in the year.

- ❏ Sow spring-flowering biennials such as forget-me-nots, sweet williams and wallflowers.

- ❏ Divide early-flowering perennials such as primulas.

- ❏ Lift spring bulbs when the foliage has died down if you need the space and can't leave them in the ground; store the bulbs in boxes in a well-ventilated place.

Weather _____

Soil Conditions _____

In Flower _____

_____

Beds & Borders _____

Greenhouse _____

Fruit & Vegetables _____

Lawn _____

Trees & Shrubs _____

Notes _____

_____

- ❏ Complete summer plantings in containers. Water containers regularly.
- ❏ Pinch out the tips of dahlias to promote bushy plants.
- ❏ Protect soft fruit from birds by throwing nets over the bushes or by building a fruit cage.
- ❏ Plant out hardened-off tender and half-hardy fuchsias into beds, borders and containers.
- ❏ Take cuttings of carnations, fuchsias, herbs and many shrubs and perennials to root in the greenhouse.

Weather _____

Soil Conditions _____

In Flower _____

_____

Beds & Borders _____

Greenhouse _____

Fruit & Vegetables _____

Lawn _____

Trees & Shrubs _____

Notes _____

_____

C H E C K L I S T

❏ Feed heathers once this month.

❏ Prune summer-flowering shrubs over three years old as they finish flowering.

❏ Cut back rock plants after flowering and trim trailing and invasive plants in the rock garden.

❏ Deadhead roses to encourage repeat flowering unless the roses are being grown for the colour and profusion of their hips.

❏ Clip fast-growing established hedges such as privet.

Weather _____

Soil Conditions _____

In Flower _____

_____

Beds & Borders _____

Greenhouse _____

Fruit & Vegetables _____

Lawn _____

Trees & Shrubs _____

Notes _____

_____

- ❏ Plant out vegetables including runner beans, cabbage, cauliflower, celery, kale and sprouting broccoli.
- ❏ Sow courgettes, marrows, pumpkins and squashes directly into their growing position.
- ❏ Lift and dry Japanese onions.
- ❏ Water early potatoes thoroughly once a week to ensure good yields.
- ❏ Plant out, water and feed outdoor tomatoes, peppers and aubergines.

Weather _____

Soil Conditions _____

In Flower _____

_____

Beds & Borders _____

Greenhouse _____

Fruit & Vegetables _____

Lawn _____

Trees & Shrubs _____

Notes _____

_____

C H E C K L I S T

- ☐ Check regularly to see if plants need water. New plantings, seedlings and plants in containers are all particularly vulnerable and may need water every day.

- ☐ Plant autumn-flowering bulbs such as amaryllis, nerines, colchicums and autumn crocuses.

- ☐ Weed and deadhead plants regularly, checking for pests and diseases at the same time.

- ☐ Feed long-flowering and late-flowering border perennials.

- ☐ Collect and sow or store ripe seeds before they fall.

Weather _____

Soil Conditions _____

In Flower _____

_____

Beds & Borders _____

Greenhouse _____

Fruit & Vegetables _____

Lawn _____

Trees & Shrubs _____

Notes _____

_____

- ❏ Adjust supports as plants grow.
- ❏ Reduce the length of wisteria tendrils by half.
- ❏ Water dahlias regularly and feed fortnightly, paying particular attention to young plants which are slow to grow.
- ❏ Harvest fruit, vegetables and herbs while they are in prime condition. Freeze, store or give away produce if you cannot use it all immediately.
- ❏ Peg down runners on strawberry plants that you want to propagate.

Weather _____

Soil Conditions _____

In Flower _____

_____

Beds & Borders _____

Greenhouse _____

Fruit & Vegetables _____

Lawn _____

Trees & Shrubs _____

Notes _____

_____

C H E C K L I S T

- ❏ Damp down the floors and staging in the greenhouse and check every day to see if plants need water.

- ❏ Lift garlic bulbs, bunch loosely and hang in an airy place to dry.

- ❏ Gather aromatic leaves and flowers to dry for pot pourri.

- ❏ Prune summer-flowering deciduous shrubs over three years old as they finish flowering.

- ❏ Mow the lawn regularly, raising the height of the cutting blades in very dry weather.

- ❏ Give roses a final feed for the year.

Weather _____

Soil Conditions _____

In Flower _____

_____

Beds & Borders _____

Greenhouse _____

Fruit & Vegetables _____

Lawn _____

Trees & Shrubs _____

Notes _____

_____

- ❏ Feed trees and shrubs that are performing badly with a high-nitrogen liquid fertiliser.
- ❏ Cut culinary herbs and dry or freeze to use later in the year.
- ❏ Feed tomato plants regularly.

- ❏ Make sure leafy vegetables such as lettuces and spinach, fruiting crops such as tomatoes and marrows, and peas and beans as their pods begin to swell, get sufficient water.
- ❏ Top up garden pools to replace water lost through evaporation.

AUGUST
WEEK 1

Weather _____

Soil Conditions _____

In Flower _____

_____

Beds & Borders _____

Greenhouse _____

Fruit & Vegetables _____

Lawn _____

Trees & Shrubs _____

Notes _____

_____

C H E C K L I S T

- ❏ Organise basic care for your garden before you go away on holiday. Watering and harvesting are the tasks that need very regular attention.

- ❏ Pinch out the growing tips of wallflowers for bushy plants.

- ❏ Deadhead regularly to encourage more flowers unless you want seeds or hips to form.

- ❏ Order spring-flowering bulbs to plant in the autumn.

- ❏ Check containers every day to see if they need watering.

Weather _____

Soil Conditions _____

In Flower _____

_____

Beds & Borders _____

Greenhouse _____

Fruit & Vegetables _____

Lawn _____

Trees & Shrubs _____

Notes _____

_____

- ❏ Apply a high-potash liquid feed to dahlias, water regularly and tie in new growth to stakes.
- ❏ Prune espalier and cordon-grown apple and pear trees.
- ❏ Plant summer varieties of strawberries to crop next year.

- ❏ Start off the first spring cabbages.
- ❏ Remove the growing tips of tomato plants in the greenhouse to encourage rapid development of the fruits on the top trusses.
- ❏ Hand weed heather beds and replace mulch if necessary.

Weather _____

Soil Conditions _____

In Flower _____

_____

Beds & Borders _____

Greenhouse _____

Fruit & Vegetables _____

Lawn _____

Trees & Shrubs _____

Notes _____

_____

C H E C K L I S T

- ❑ Give conifer hedges their annual trim and reduce the growth on new spring-planted conifers to make a thicker hedge.
- ❑ Check for reversion on variegated shrubs and trees and remove all-green shoots.
- ❑ Plant dwarf bulbous irises for winter colour.
- ❑ Tidy the pool by deadheading marginal aquatic plants and removing excess growth from submerged oxygenating plants.

Weather _____

Soil Conditions _____

In Flower _____

_____

Beds & Borders _____

Greenhouse _____

Fruit & Vegetables _____

Lawn _____

Trees & Shrubs _____

Notes _____

_____

- ❏ Check regularly to see if plants need water. Hanging baskets and small containers may need watering every day.
- ❏ Sow overwintering onions, such as Japanese varieties, for harvesting early next summer.
- ❏ Prune summer-flowering shrubs over three years old as they finish flowering.
- ❏ Repair, clean and disinfect the greenhouse during the quiet summer period, putting all the plants outside temporarily.

SUMMER
NOTES

AUTUMN

I'm going out to clean the pasture spring;

I'll only stop to rake the leaves away

(And wait to watch the water clear, I may):

I shan't be gone long. – You come too.

—Robert Frost, *The Pasture*

'Do bulbs live a long time?...'
inquired Mary anxiously.
'They're things as helps themselves,'
said Martha.
'...If you don't trouble 'em,
most of 'em'll work away
underground for a lifetime
an' spread out an' have
little 'uns.'

—Frances Hodgson Burnett
The Secret Garden

LISTEN!
THE WIND IS RISING,
AND THE AIR IS WILD
WITH LEAVES,

WE HAVE HAD OUR
SUMMER EVENINGS,
NOW FOR
OCTOBER EVES!

—Humbert Wolfe
Autumn (Resignation)

Weather _____

Soil Conditions _____

In Flower _____

_____

Beds & Borders _____

Greenhouse _____

Fruit & Vegetables _____

Lawn _____

Trees & Shrubs _____

Notes _____

_____

C H E C K L I S T

- ❑ Sow hardy annuals to be over-wintered outdoors and in the greenhouse.

- ❑ Plant out spring-flowering biennials, including forget-me-nots and wallflowers, in their flowering positions to give them time to establish before winter.

- ❑ Plant prepared bulbs in bowls for indoor display at Christmas and early next year.

- ❑ Continue to water containers every day if necessary.

- ❑ Plant new border perennials and water the plants in well.

SEPTEMBER

WEEK 2

Weather _____

Soil Conditions _____

In Flower _____

_____

Beds & Borders _____

Greenhouse _____

Fruit & Vegetables _____

Lawn _____

Trees & Shrubs _____

Notes _____

_____

❏ Prune deciduous autumn-flowering shrubs over three years old as they finish flowering.

❏ Pick apples and pears as they ripen and store the excess.

❏ Plant windowboxes and pots for winter interest.

❏ Apply or renew greasebands on the trunks of apple and pear trees.

❏ Remove shading wash from the greenhouse if applied in the spring.

❏ Sow parsley and chervil for use in late winter and early spring.

Weather _____

Soil Conditions _____

In Flower _____

_____

Beds & Borders _____

Greenhouse _____

Fruit & Vegetables _____

Lawn _____

Trees & Shrubs _____

Notes _____

_____

C H E C K L I S T

❏ Divide and replant large clumps of perennial herbs.

❏ Plant bearded, beardless and bulbous irises in prepared sites.

❏ Raise the cutting height on lawnmowers as the growth rate of the grass slows.

❏ Start to plant spring-flowering bulbs in borders and in containers, giving priority to daffodils as they begin their root growth earlier than other bulbs.

❏ Take pelargonium cuttings to overwinter indoors.

Weather _____

Soil Conditions _____

In Flower _____

_____

Beds & Borders _____

Greenhouse _____

Fruit & Vegetables _____

Lawn _____

Trees & Shrubs _____

Notes _____

_____

❏ Cover summer bedding with several layers of horticultural fleece if frost is forecast to prolong the display a little longer.

❏ Lift tender perennials such as argyranthemums, fuchsias and pelargoniums before the first frost to be overwintered under cover.

❏ Scarify the lawn vigorously to remove dead moss and grass then spike if the soil is compacted.

❏ If the lawn is in poor condition apply an autumn fertiliser to boost root growth.

❏ Give hedges a final trim.

Weather _____

Soil Conditions _____

In Flower _____

_____

Beds & Borders _____

Greenhouse _____

Fruit & Vegetables _____

Lawn _____

Trees & Shrubs _____

Notes _____

_____

C H E C K L I S T

- ❏ Take cuttings of tender plants to overwinter indoors.
- ❏ Put a net over the pool to prevent leaves falling in and polluting the water.
- ❏ Plant tulips and hyacinths for spring flowering.

- ❏ Top dress established borders with well-rotted garden compost or manure.
- ❏ Clean barbecues, garden furniture and non-frost-resistant pots and store them for the winter.
- ❏ Plant garlic cloves.

Weather _____

Soil Conditions _____

In Flower _____

_____

Beds & Borders _____

Greenhouse _____

Fruit & Vegetables _____

Lawn _____

Trees & Shrubs _____

Notes _____

_____

❏ Plant new climbers, shrubs and trees while the soil is still warm.

❏ Clear out summer containers, taking cuttings or saving tender plants if you have space to overwinter them.

❏ Check the greenhouse heating and insulate to save heat.

❏ Stop feeding and reduce watering for plants in the greenhouse.

❏ Make sure bowls of bulbs being forced for indoor flowering do not dry out.

OCTOBER
WEEK 3

Weather   _____

Soil Conditions   _____

In Flower   _____

_____

Beds & Borders   _____

Greenhouse   _____

Fruit & Vegetables   _____

Lawn   _____

Trees & Shrubs   _____

Notes   _____

_____

C H E C K L I S T

- ☐ Cut down the top growth of dahlias when it is blackened by frost then lift and dry the tubers for storage.

- ☐ Remove half-hardy fuchsias from the garden and from containers and hanging baskets and put them in pots to overwinter under cover.

- ☐ Clear fallen leaves and recycle them to make leafmould.

- ☐ Bring in perlargoniums before the first frost and keep in a light frost-free place over the winter.

- ☐ Prune rambling and summer-flowering climbing roses.

Weather _____

Soil Conditions _____

In Flower _____

_____

Beds & Borders _____

Greenhouse _____

Fruit & Vegetables _____

Lawn _____

Trees & Shrubs _____

Notes _____

_____

❏ Begin winter digging, adding well-rotted organic matter to improve the soil.

❏ Complete the planting of all new evergreens including conifers.

❏ Lift and store maincrop carrots and potatoes.

❏ Divide and replant waterside plants such as astilbes and trollius.

❏ Finish planting up containers for the spring.

❏ Prune autumn-flowering deciduous shrubs over three years old as they finish flowering.

Weather   _____

Soil Conditions   _____

In Flower   _____

_____

Beds & Borders   _____

Greenhouse   _____

Fruit & Vegetables   _____

Lawn   _____

Trees & Shrubs   _____

Notes   _____

_____

C H E C K L I S T

- ☐ Put winter protection in place around vulnerable border perennials and shrubs.

- ☐ Tidy borders for the winter by removing stakes, cutting back dying foliage and digging out perennial weeds.

- ☐ Cut the lawn for the last time this year and clean and store the lawnmower.

- ☐ Prune wisteria to increase flowering next year.

- ☐ Lift begonia tubers, dry them then store in a cool, frost-free place.

Weather _____

Soil Conditions _____

In Flower _____

_____

Beds & Borders _____

Greenhouse _____

Fruit & Vegetables _____

Lawn _____

Trees & Shrubs _____

Notes _____

_____

- ❏ Prepare for autumn and winter winds by removing decaying or dead branches on established trees.
- ❏ Protect newly planted evergreens with a temporary windbreak until they are established.
- ❏ Group containers for mutual protection over winter, wrapping up vulnerable pots and plants.
- ❏ Start planting bare-root fruit trees and bushes.
- ❏ Ventilate the greenhouse on sunny days.

Weather _____

Soil Conditions _____

In Flower _____

_____

Beds & Borders _____

Greenhouse _____

Fruit & Vegetables _____

Lawn _____

Trees & Shrubs _____

Notes _____

_____

C H E C K L I S T

❑ Move bowls of bulbs being forced for indoor flowering into a light but cool position when the leaves are about 2.5 cm (1 in) high.

❑ Clear fallen leaves and other debris so slugs, snails and other pests have nowhere to hide.

❑ Shorten hybrid tea roses and floribundas to reduce the damage from windrock.

❑ Cut back one-third of the summer's growth on hardy fuchsias leaving the remaining bare stems as protection over the winter.

Weather _____

Soil Conditions _____

In Flower _____

_____

Beds & Borders _____

Greenhouse _____

Fruit & Vegetables _____

Lawn _____

Trees & Shrubs _____

Notes _____

_____

- ❏ Plant bare-root and container-grown roses and transplant any established roses you want to resite.

- ❏ Create an inexpensive hedge by taking hardwood cuttings and inserting them directly into the growing site.

- ❏ Prune autumn-flowering shrubs over three years old as they finish flowering.

- ❏ Drain surface pumps in the pond and have them serviced if necessary; otherwise clean, dry and grease before storing.

P LANT   P ROFILES

Plant name _____

❏ *Annual/Biennial*   ❏ *Perennial*   ❏ *Bulb, corm, tuber*   ❏ *Shrub/Tree*
❏ *Seed*   ❏ *Seedling*   ❏ *Bare-root*   ❏ *Container-grown*

Where purchased _____

Date received _____   *Condition upon arrival* _____

Where planted _____

Height at maturity _____   *Spread at maturity* _____

Season and colour of flowers _____

How it performed _____

Plant name _____

❏ *Annual/Biennial*   ❏ *Perennial*   ❏ *Bulb, corm, tuber*   ❏ *Shrub/Tree*
❏ *Seed*   ❏ *Seedling*   ❏ *Bare-root*   ❏ *Container-grown*

Where purchased _____

Date received _____   *Condition upon arrival* _____

Where planted _____

Height at maturity _____   *Spread at maturity* _____

Season and colour of flowers _____

How it performed _____

Plant name _____

❏ Annual/Biennial   ❏ Perennial   ❏ Bulb, corm, tuber   ❏ Shrub/Tree
❏ Seed   ❏ Seedling   ❏ Bare-root   ❏ Container-grown

Where purchased _____

Date received _____   Condition upon arrival _____

Where planted _____

Height at maturity _____   Spread at maturity _____

Season and colour of flowers _____

How it performed _____

Plant name _____

❏ Annual/Biennial   ❏ Perennial   ❏ Bulb, corm, tuber   ❏ Shrub/Tree
❏ Seed   ❏ Seedling   ❏ Bare-root   ❏ Container-grown

Where purchased _____

Date received _____   Condition upon arrival _____

Where planted _____

Height at maturity _____   Spread at maturity _____

Season and colour of flowers _____

How it performed _____

PLANT PROFILES

Plant name _____

❏ *Annual/Biennial*   ❏ *Perennial*   ❏ *Bulb, corm, tuber*   ❏ *Shrub/Tree*
❏ *Seed*   ❏ *Seedling*   ❏ *Bare-root*   ❏ *Container-grown*

Where purchased _____

Date received _____   *Condition upon arrival* _____

Where planted _____

Height at maturity _____   *Spread at maturity* _____

Season and colour of flowers _____

How it performed _____

Plant name _____

❏ *Annual/Biennial*   ❏ *Perennial*   ❏ *Bulb, corm, tuber*   ❏ *Shrub/Tree*
❏ *Seed*   ❏ *Seedling*   ❏ *Bare-root*   ❏ *Container-grown*

Where purchased _____

Date received _____   *Condition upon arrival* _____

Where planted _____

Height at maturity _____   *Spread at maturity* _____

Season and colour of flowers _____

How it performed _____

Plant name _____

❑ *Annual/Biennial*　❑ *Perennial*　❑ *Bulb, corm, tuber*　❑ *Shrub/Tree*
❑ *Seed*　　　❑ *Seedling*　　　❑ *Bare-root*　　　❑ *Container-grown*

Where purchased _____

Date received _____　*Condition upon arrival* _____

Where planted _____

Height at maturity _____　*Spread at maturity* _____

Season and colour of flowers _____

How it performed _____

Plant name _____

❑ *Annual/Biennial*　❑ *Perennial*　❑ *Bulb, corm, tuber*　❑ *Shrub/Tree*
❑ *Seed*　　　❑ *Seedling*　　　❑ *Bare-root*　　　❑ *Container-grown*

Where purchased _____

Date received _____　*Condition upon arrival* _____

Where planted _____

Height at maturity _____　*Spread at maturity* _____

Season and colour of flowers _____

How it performed _____

PLANT PROFILES

Plant name _____

❏ Annual/Biennial   ❏ Perennial   ❏ Bulb, corm, tuber   ❏ Shrub/Tree
❏ Seed   ❏ Seedling   ❏ Bare-root   ❏ Container-grown

Where purchased _____

Date received _____   Condition upon arrival _____

Where planted _____

Height at maturity _____   Spread at maturity _____

Season and colour of flowers _____

How it performed _____

Plant name _____

❏ Annual/Biennial   ❏ Perennial   ❏ Bulb, corm, tuber   ❏ Shrub/Tree
❏ Seed   ❏ Seedling   ❏ Bare-root   ❏ Container-grown

Where purchased _____

Date received _____   Condition upon arrival _____

Where planted _____

Height at maturity _____   Spread at maturity _____

Season and colour of flowers _____

How it performed _____

Plant name _____

☐ *Annual/Biennial* ☐ *Perennial* ☐ *Bulb, corm, tuber* ☐ *Shrub/Tree*
☐ *Seed* ☐ *Seedling* ☐ *Bare-root* ☐ *Container-grown*

Where purchased _____

Date received _____ *Condition upon arrival* _____

Where planted _____

Height at maturity _____ *Spread at maturity* _____

Season and colour of flowers _____

How it performed _____

Plant name _____

☐ *Annual/Biennial* ☐ *Perennial* ☐ *Bulb, corm, tuber* ☐ *Shrub/Tree*
☐ *Seed* ☐ *Seedling* ☐ *Bare-root* ☐ *Container-grown*

Where purchased _____

Date received _____ *Condition upon arrival* _____

Where planted _____

Height at maturity _____ *Spread at maturity* _____

Season and colour of flowers _____

How it performed _____

FRUIT & VEGETABLE PROFILES

Crop _____

Variety _____ Date planted _____

❏ Annual   ❏ Perennial   ❏ Bush   ❏ Tree   ❏ Vine
❏ Seed   ❏ Seedling   ❏ Bare-root   ❏ Container-grown

Where purchased _____

Where planted _____

Feeding _____ Problems _____

Date of harvest _____ Yield _____

Quality _____

Crop _____

Variety _____ Date planted _____

❏ Annual   ❏ Perennial   ❏ Bush   ❏ Tree   ❏ Vine
❏ Seed   ❏ Seedling   ❏ Bare-root   ❏ Container-grown

Where purchased _____

Where planted _____

Feeding _____ Problems _____

Date of harvest _____ Yield _____

Quality _____

Crop _____

Variety _____ *Date planted* _____

❏ *Annual*   ❏ *Perennial*   ❏ *Bush*   ❏ *Tree*   ❏ *Vine*

❏ *Seed*   ❏ *Seedling*   ❏ *Bare-root*   ❏ *Container-grown*

Where purchased _____

Where planted _____

Feeding _____ *Problems* _____

Date of harvest _____ *Yield* _____

Quality _____

Crop _____

Variety _____ *Date planted* _____

❏ *Annual*   ❏ *Perennial*   ❏ *Bush*   ❏ *Tree*   ❏ *Vine*

❏ *Seed*   ❏ *Seedling*   ❏ *Bare-root*   ❏ *Container-grown*

Where purchased _____

Where planted _____

Feeding _____ *Problems* _____

Date of harvest _____ *Yield* _____

Quality _____

FRUIT & VEGETABLE PROFILES

Crop _____

Variety _____ Date planted _____

❏ Annual   ❏ Perennial   ❏ Bush   ❏ Tree   ❏ Vine
❏ Seed   ❏ Seedling   ❏ Bare-root   ❏ Container-grown

Where purchased _____

Where planted _____

Feeding _____ Problems _____

Date of harvest _____ Yield _____

Quality _____

Crop _____

Variety _____ Date planted _____

❏ Annual   ❏ Perennial   ❏ Bush   ❏ Tree   ❏ Vine
❏ Seed   ❏ Seedling   ❏ Bare-root   ❏ Container-grown

Where purchased _____

Where planted _____

Feeding _____ Problems _____

Date of harvest _____ Yield _____

Quality _____

Crop _____

Variety _____ *Date planted* _____

❏ *Annual* ❏ *Perennial* ❏ *Bush* ❏ *Tree* ❏ *Vine*
❏ *Seed* ❏ *Seedling* ❏ *Bare-root* ❏ *Container-grown*

Where purchased _____

Where planted _____

Feeding _____ *Problems* _____

Date of harvest _____ *Yield* _____

Quality _____

Crop _____

Variety _____ *Date planted* _____

❏ *Annual* ❏ *Perennial* ❏ *Bush* ❏ *Tree* ❏ *Vine*
❏ *Seed* ❏ *Seedling* ❏ *Bare-root* ❏ *Container-grown*

Where purchased _____

Where planted _____

Feeding _____ *Problems* _____

Date of harvest _____ *Yield* _____

Quality _____

FRUIT & VEGETABLE PROFILES

Crop _____

Variety _____ Date planted _____

❏ Annual   ❏ Perennial   ❏ Bush   ❏ Tree   ❏ Vine
❏ Seed   ❏ Seedling   ❏ Bare-root   ❏ Container-grown

Where purchased _____

Where planted _____

Feeding_____ Problems_____

Date of harvest _____ Yield _____

Quality _____

Crop _____

Variety _____ Date planted _____

❏ Annual   ❏ Perennial   ❏ Bush   ❏ Tree   ❏ Vine
❏ Seed   ❏ Seedling   ❏ Bare-root   ❏ Container-grown

Where purchased _____

Where planted _____

Feeding_____ Problems_____

Date of harvest _____ Yield _____

Quality _____